Hayley Westenra Pure

WISE PUBLICATIONS
part of The Music Sales Group
London / New York / Paris / Sydney / Copenhagen / Berlin / Madrid / Tokyo

Exclusive distributors:

Music Sales Limited
8/9 Frith Street, London,
W1D 3JB, England.

Music Sales Pty Limited
120 Rothschild Avenue, Rosebery,
NSW 2018, Australia.

Order No. AM979946
ISBN 1-84449-469-1
This book © Copyright 2004 by Wise Publications.

Music arrangements by Paul Honey/Quentin Thomas.
Music processed by Note-orious Productions Limited.

Printed in the United Kingdom by
Caligraving Limited, Thetford, Norfolk.

www.musicsales.com

Pokarekare Ana

Traditional
Arranged by Sarah Class

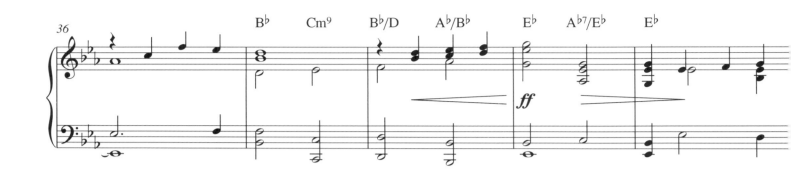

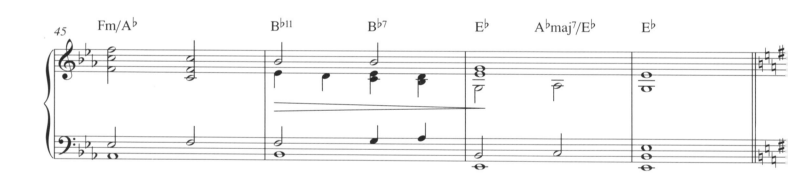

E hi - ne e, Ho - ki mai - ra.

8

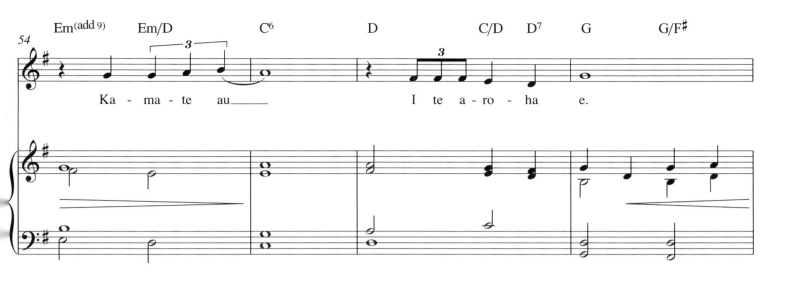

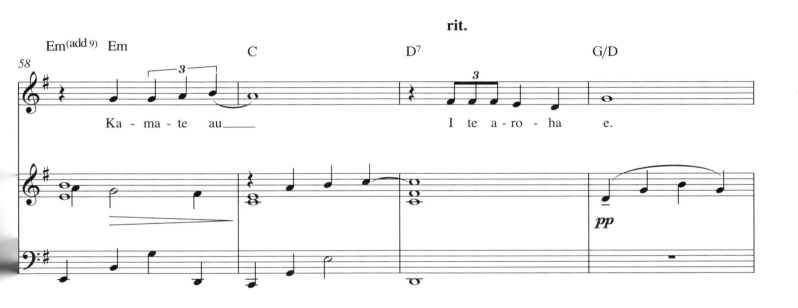

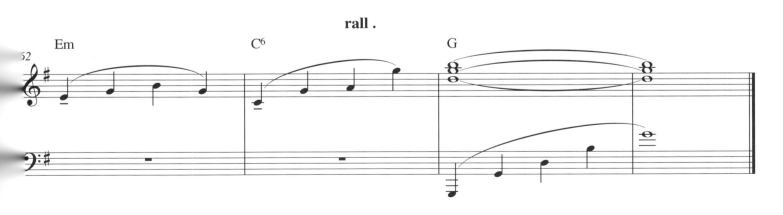

9

Who Painted The Moon Black?

Words & Music by Sonia Aletta Nel
Arranged by Sarah Class

It must have been the dark - est night, not e - ven a star in sight, just as you walked a - way from me, now. Who paint - ed the moon black? Just when you passed your love back.

13

14

River Of Dreams

Music by Antonio Vivaldi
Words by Charlie Dore
Arranged by Sarah Class

Ri - ver of dreams take me with you to - night, ly - ing in your arms we'll__

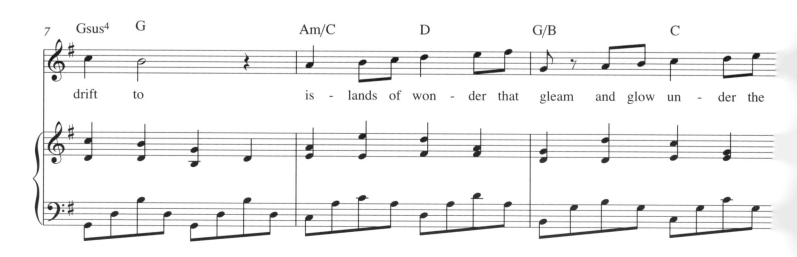

drift to is - lands of won - der that gleam and glow un - der the

make me a part of you, deep in the heart of you, let my re-flec-tion be clear in the wa-ter of life._____ That tum-bles as it turns a-gain to -wards_____ the night.

morendo

20

Hine e Hine

Words & Music by Princess Te Rangi Pai
Arranged by Sarah Class

Dark Waltz

Words & Music by Matteo Saggese, Umberto Morasca & Frank Musker

Dance me in - to the night, un - der - neath the moon___ shin - ing so bright.___

Turn - ing me in - to the light.___

Verse 2:

Time dancers whirling past
I gaze through the looking glass
And feel just beyond my grasp is heaven.

Sacred geometry
Where movement is poetry,
Visions of you and me forever.

Dance me into the night, *etc.*

Amazing Grace

Words by John Newton
Music: Traditional
Arranged by George Martin

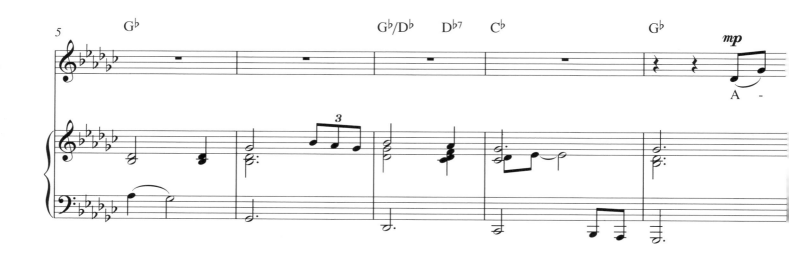

saved a wretch like me. I

once was lost but now I'm

found, was blind but now I see.

'Twas grace that taught my

heart   to fear,   and___ grace,   my___

sim.

fears   re - lieved._____ How__ pre - cious__

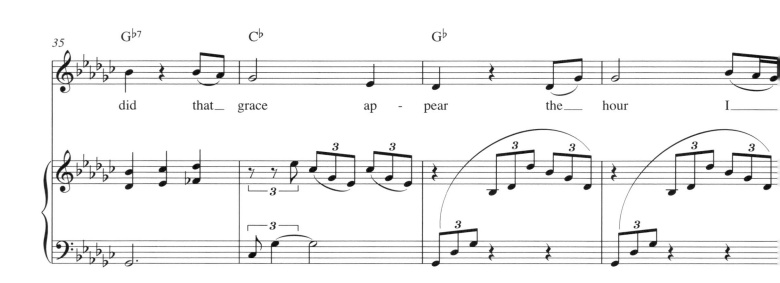

did   that__ grace   ap - pear   the__ hour   I

when we've____ first be - gun,_____ than____ when we've____ first be - gun._____

Beat Of Your Heart

Words & Music by George Martin & Giles Martin

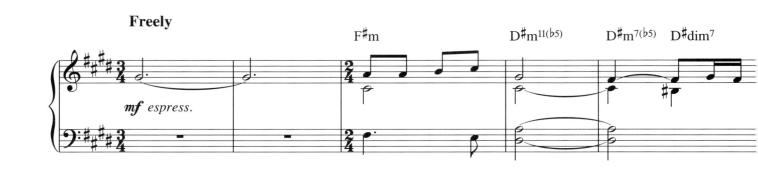

Car - ry me_ a - way_ from_ this dark_ and lone - ly room,_
(Verse 2: See block lyric)

heart.   I've found all my dreams___ in the beat,

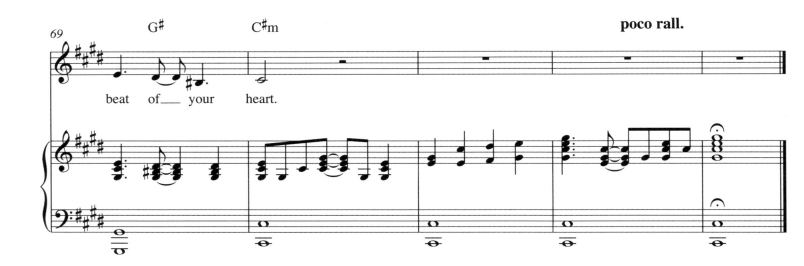

beat of___ your heart.

Verse 2:

Picture book of memories, how we used to be,
Some people spend a lifetime waiting for their dreams.
But I won't find the answers by looking at the stars,
I can find my strength in the beat of your heart.

Heaven

Words & Music by Ronan Hardiman & Frank Musker

Verse 2:

So why, tell me why the good die young my old friend,
I pray that heaven waits for everyone in the end.
And love, love is how we cross that bridge to the light,
A star that is what you are in my darkest night.
Be always by my side.

Heaven, heaven, ooh, waiting there for me, *etc.*

Wuthering Heights

Words & Music by Kate Bush
Arranged by Sarah Class

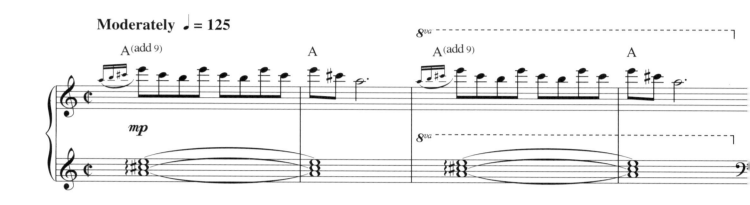

Out on the wile - y, wind - y moors__ we'd__ roll and fall in green.
(Verse 2: See block lyric)

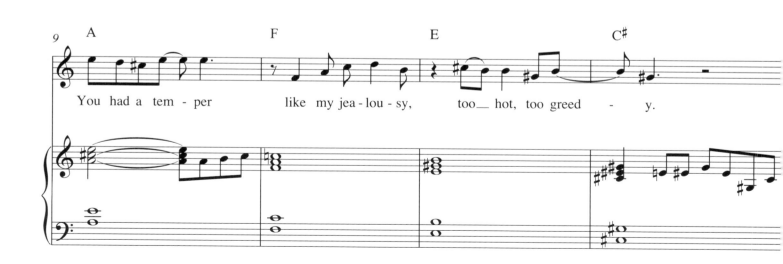

You had a tem - per like my jea - lou - sy, too__ hot, too greed - y.

Verse 2:

Ooh, it gets dark! It gets lonely,
On the other side from you.
I pine a lot. I find the lot
Falls through without you.
I'm coming back, love.
Cruel Heathcliff, my one dream,
My only master.

Too long I roam in the night.
I'm coming back to his side, to put it right.
I'm coming home to wuthering, wuthering,
Wuthering Heights,

Heathcliff, it's me, Cathy *etc.*

51

Ave Maria

By Franz Schubert

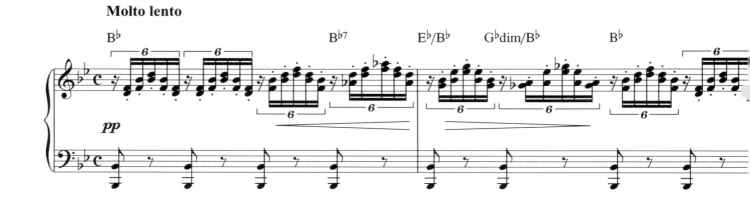

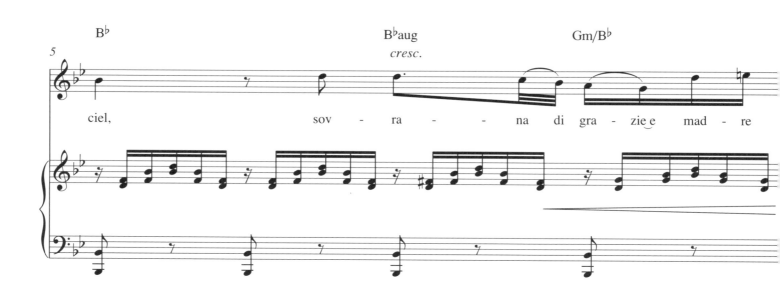

Ave Maria

By J. S. Bach/Charles Gounod

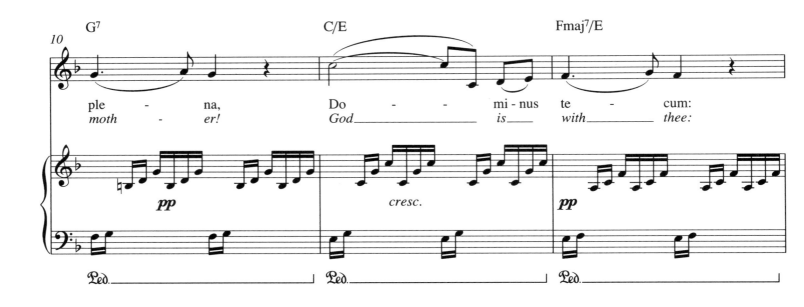

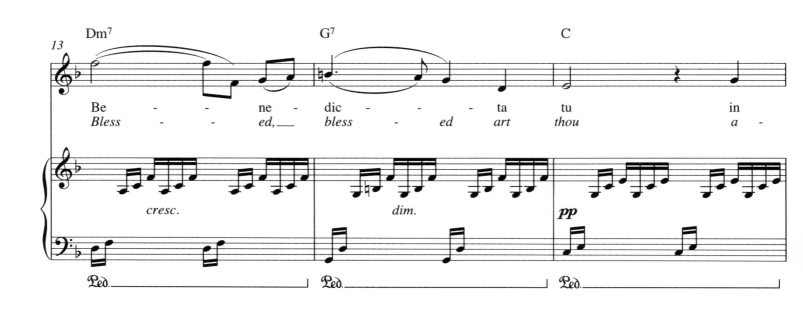

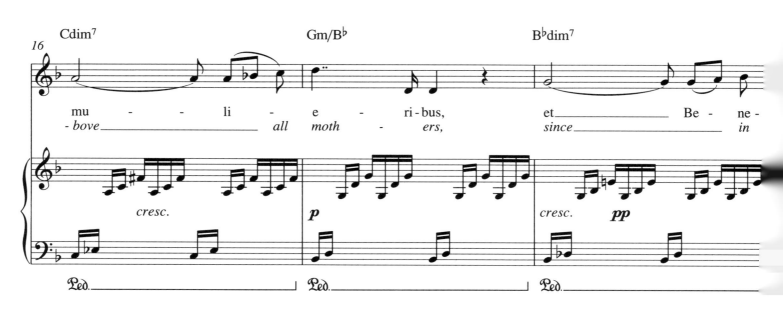

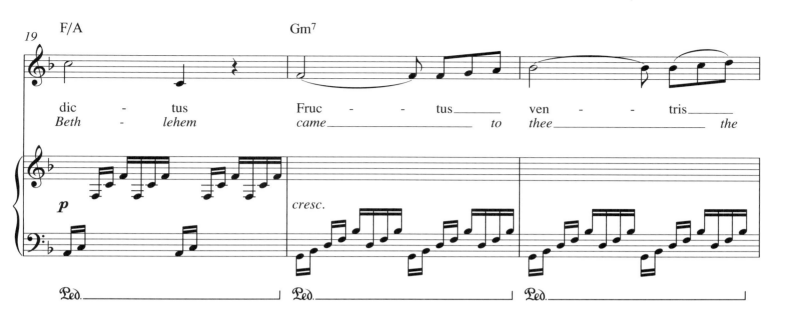

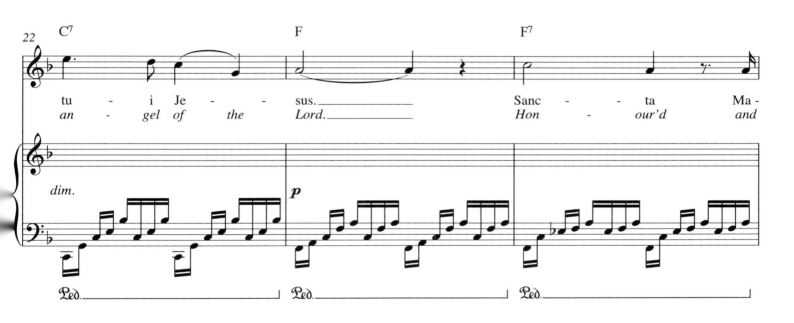

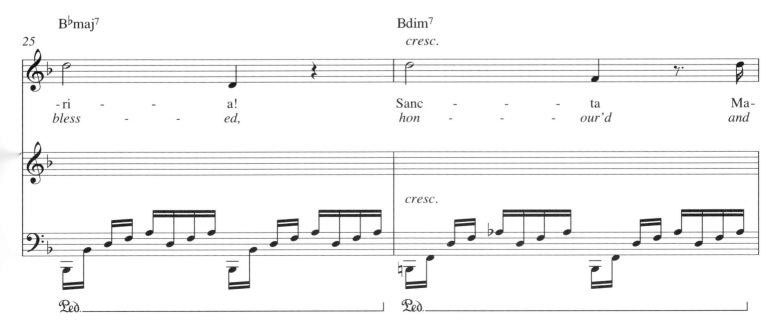

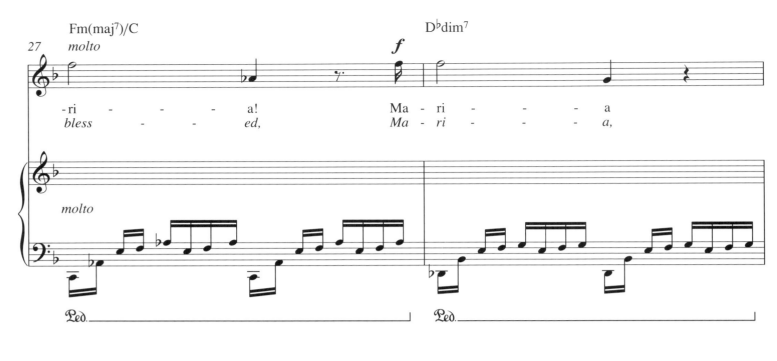

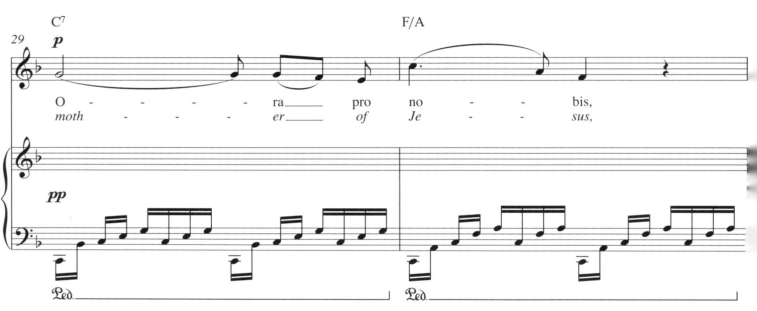

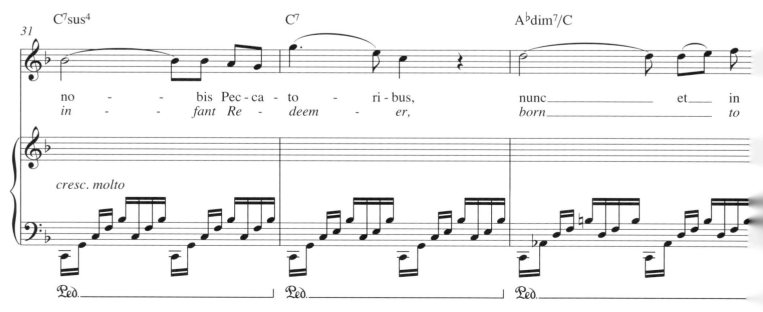

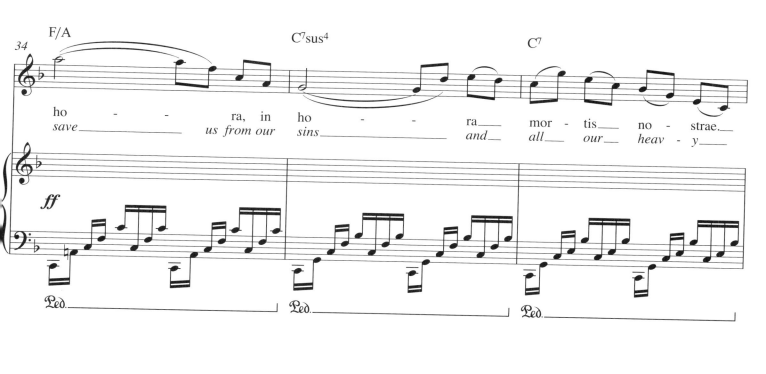

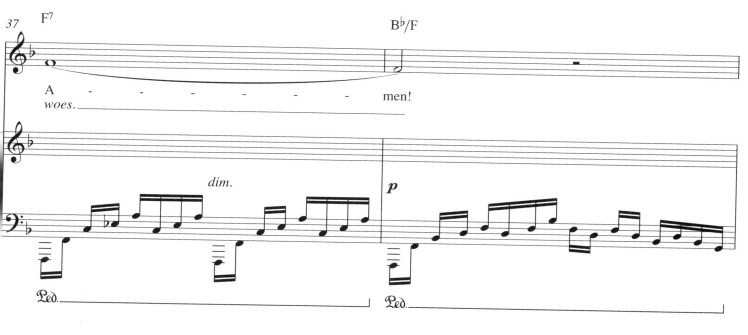

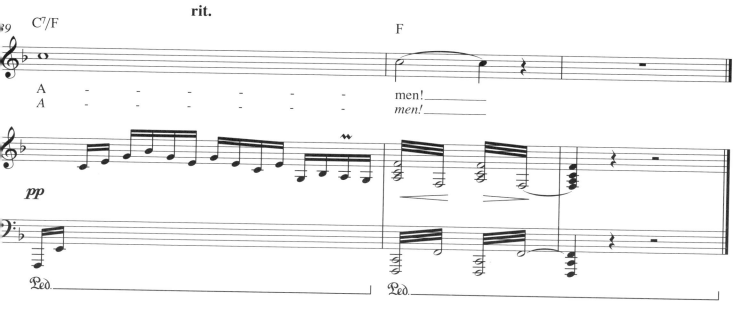

Wishing You Were Somehow Here Again

Music by Andrew Lloyd Webber
Lyrics by Charles Hart
Additional Lyrics by Richard Stilgoe

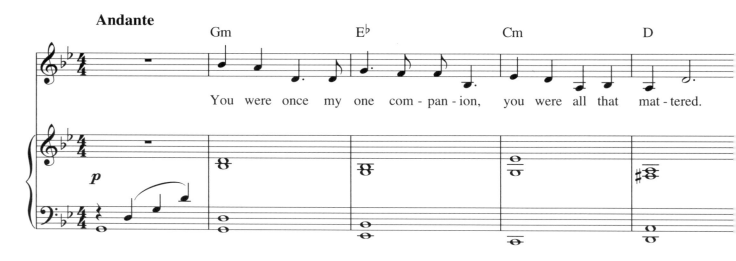

You were once my one com-pan-ion, you were all that mat-tered.

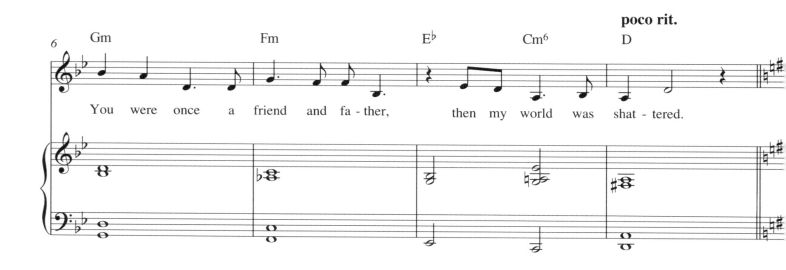

You were once a friend and fa-ther, then my world was shat-tered.

Wish-ing you were some-how here a-gain, wish-ing you were some-how

Passing bells and sculpted angels, cold and monumental,

seem for you the wrong companions; you were warm and gentle.

Too many years, fighting back tears, why can't the past just die?